DOODLE a picture of YOURSELF on the day you START this book.

MEOW!
What does this curious kitty
see inside the cage?

Guess Who?

ADD FACES to these MYSTERY CHARACTERS.

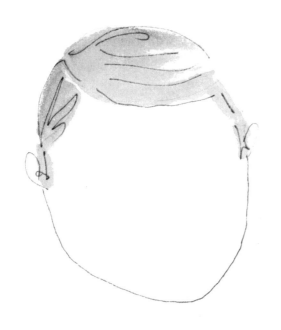

Doodle something totally... HILARIOUS.

LEARN TO DRAW

Follow the steps below to draw a **SILLY SQUIRREL** and a HANDSOME HEDGEHOG.

| step 1 | step 2 | step 3 | You try it! |

Woof! Woof!

Dance Party!

SHE SAID WHAT?!

Doodle the messages on these cell phones.

WHAT COMES NEXT?

Finish these SWEET PATTERNS.

DESIGN some original **DOODLE PATTERNS** of your own!

Once Upon a Time...

BEST FRIENDS FOREVER!

Fill the frames with doodles of you and your fabulous friends.

LEARN TO ♥ DRAW

Follow the steps below to draw a DASHING DEER and a FROLICKING FOX.

step 1	step 2	step 3	You try it!

CHECK OUT THIS DOODLE-RIFIC ALPHABET!

A B C D E F G H I J K L M N
O P Q R S T U V W X Y Z . ! ? ,

TRACE the letters and words below.

A B C D E F G H I J K L M N
O P Q R S T U V W X Y Z . ! ? ,

BRILLIANT   CREATIVE   SILLY   IMAGINE

Use what you've learned to **DOODLE WORDS OF YOUR OWN!**

Where would you go on your **DREAM VACATION?**

PHOTO BOOTH

YOU'RE A STAR!

If you and your BFF could pose with celebrities, who would they be? Doodle each shot in the photo frames.

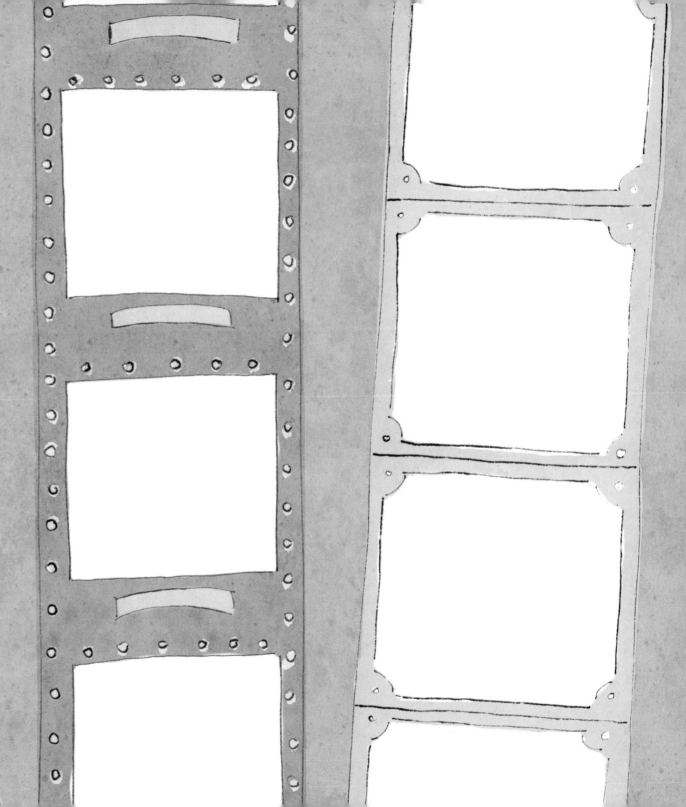

Doodle everything you can think of that's... Purple.

LEARN TO DRAW

Follow the steps below to draw a **PINE TREE** and a **FRIENDLY OWL**.

step 1	step 2	step 3	You try it!

My Royal Kingdom

LOOK VERY CLOSELY...
What do you see in this crystal ball?

TRACE and COLOR all of the food you LOVE...

TRACE and COLOR all of the food you LOATHE...

yuck

Pasta

POPCORN

CHOCOLATE

Pizza!

TOMATO SAUCE

FRENCH FRIES

Fill in these **WORDS** with **DOODLES.**

SPARKLY CUTE

DIVA STYLIN'

CHIC

ABSOLUTELY

FABULOUS

FASHIONISTA OH BABY!

a Day in the Life of _____

Doodle an original comic strip about an out-of-the-ordinary day.

WHAT COMES NEXT?

Finish these **NATURE PATTERNS.**

DESIGN some original DOODLE PATTERNS of your own!

Doodle everything you can think of that's... ORANGE.

LEARN TO ♥ DRAW

Follow the steps below to draw a **NOT-SO-QUICK TORTOISE** and a **PLAYFUL PUP.**

step 1	step 2	step 3	You try it!

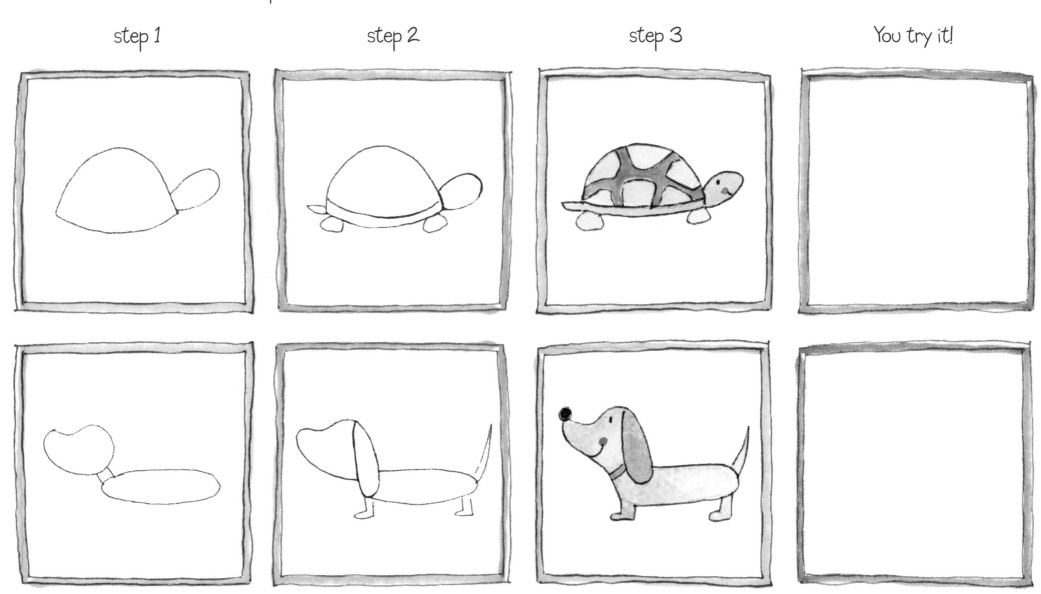

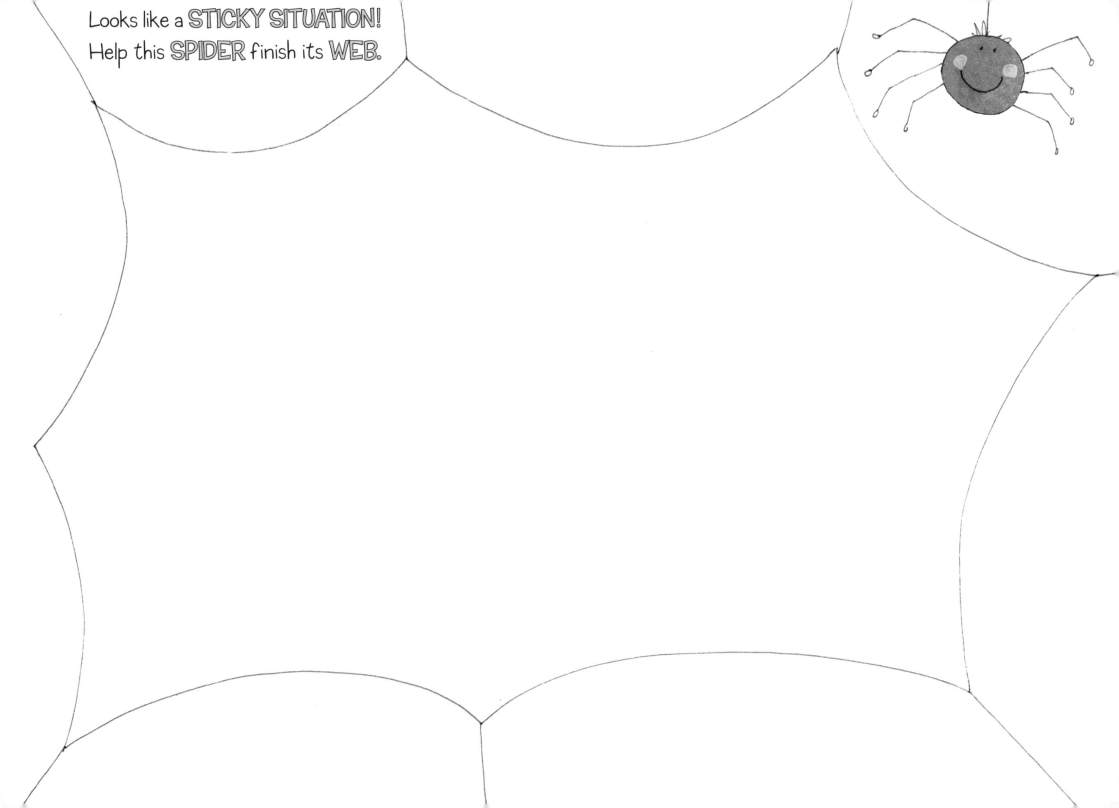

Looks like a **STICKY SITUATION!**
Help this **SPIDER** finish its **WEB.**

Fill in these **WORDS** with **DOODLES.**

BEAUTIFUL CREATIVE

SMART

UNIQUE IMAGINE

PRECIOUS

YOU ROCK! ARTSY

Is it a bird? Is it a plane?

CHECK OUT THIS *Fancy-Schmancy* ALPHABET!

Aa Bb Cc Dd Ee Ff Gg Hh Ii Jj Kk Ll Mm Nn

Oo Pp Qq Rr Ss Tt Uu Vv Ww Xx Yy Zz . ! ? ,

TRACE the letters and words below.

Aa Bb Cc Dd Ee Ff Gg Hh Ii Jj Kk Ll Mm Nn

Oo Pp Qq Rr Ss Tt Uu Vv Ww Xx Yy Zz . ! ? ,

Fabulous   Glitzy   Sublime   Stylin'

Use what you've learned to DOODLE WORDS OF YOUR OWN!

LEARN TO ♥ DRAW

Follow the steps below to draw a **CUTE KITTY** and a TEENY-TINY MOUSE.

step 1　　　　　step 2　　　　　step 3　　　　　You try it!

Doodle a picture of **YOURSELF** in the **FUTURE**.

IT'S A VERY IMPORTANT DATE!
Complete this official invitation!

You are Cordially Invited

To: _____
From: _____

PHOTO BOOTH

If you took your **FAMILY PORTRAIT** in a photo booth, what would the session look like? Doodle each shot in the photo frames.

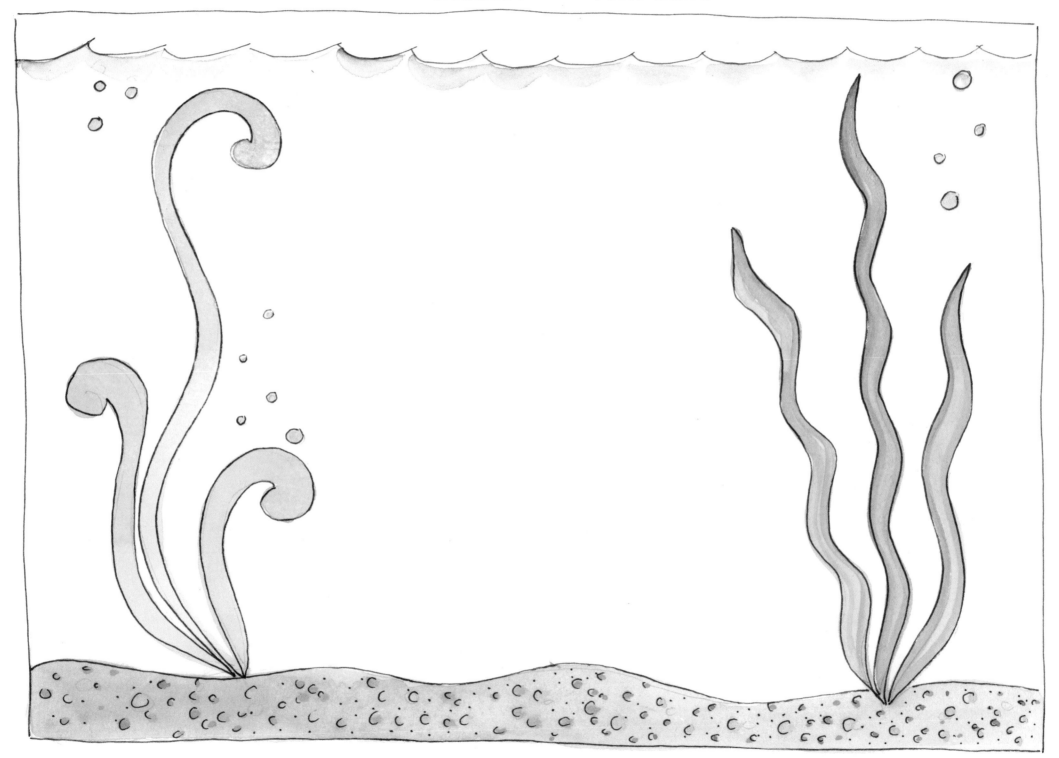

WHAT A PUP!

Complete each dog.

LEARN TO DRAW

Follow the steps below to draw a **HAPPY HAMSTER** and a **CHATTY PARROT**.

step 1 step 2 step 3 You try it!

TIME TO HIT THE CAFETERIA!

What's for lunch?

TWEET! TWEET!

What's the word on the street?

WHO'S IN YOUR FAMILY TREE?

Fill the frames with doodles of you and your family members.

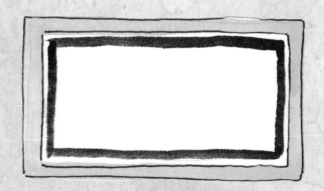

DOODLE THIS DOG...

UPSIDE DOWN

BACKWARDS

WITH YOUR EYES CLOSED

A GIFT OR TWO
FROM ME, TO YOU!
Design some eye-catching gift wrap.

FAIRY POWER!
Doodle a super-magical place
for us to live.

Doodle something...

LEARN TO DRAW

Follow the steps below to draw a BIRTHDAY BANNER and a COLORFUL CUPCAKE.

step 1	step 2	step 3	You try it!

What's on this pizza?

ABSOLUTELY FABULOUS!

Doodle a **BIRTHDAY PARTY!**

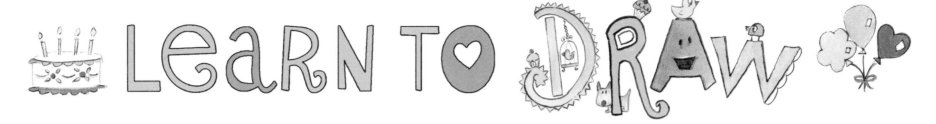

LEARN TO ♥ DRAW

Follow the steps below to draw a YUMMY CAKE and SHAPED BALLOONS.

step 1	step 2	step 3	You try it!

PLAY WITH YOUR FOOD!
Add faces to these snacks.

Doodle something... Scary.

PHOTO BOOTH

If **YOU** and **YOUR BFF** spent the day in a photo booth, what would the pictures look like?

ME AND MY BFF!

LEARN TO ♥ DRAW

Follow the steps below to draw a **FANCY PARTY HAT** and a **MATCHING PRESENT**.

step 1   step 2   step 3   You try it!

CHECK OUT THIS **BUBBLY** ALPHABET!

Aa Bb Cc Dd Ee Ff Gg Hh Ii Jj Kk Ll Mm Nn

Oo Pp Qg Rr Ss Tt Uu Vv Ww Xx Yy Zz . ! ? ,

TRACE the letters and words below.

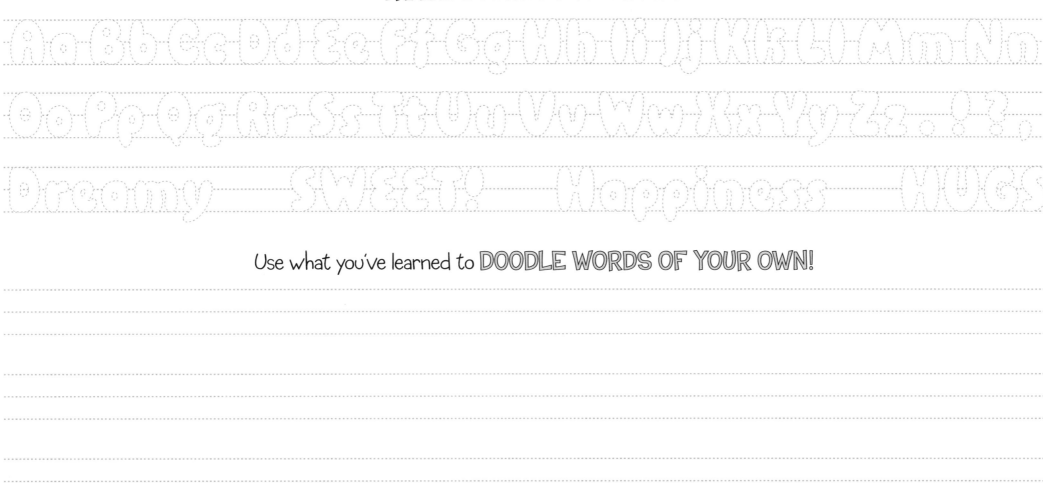

Aa Bb Cc Dd Ee Ff Gg Hh Ii Jj Kk Ll Mm Nn

Oo Pp Qg Rr Ss Tt Uu Vv Ww Xx Yy Zz . ! ? ,

Dreamy — SWEET! — Happiness — HUGS

Use what you've learned to DOODLE WORDS OF YOUR OWN!

CLEAN YOUR PLATE!
What's for dinner?

UP, UP, AND AWAY!

LEARN TO ♥ DRAW

Follow the steps below to draw a **SMILEY SNAIL** and an **ACROBATIC ANT.**

step 1	step 2	step 3	You try it!

Doodle everything you can think of that's... Blue

PURR-fectly Precious!
ADD FACES to these KITTIES.

Beep! Beep!

WHAT COMES NEXT?

Finish these DAINTY PATTERNS.

DESIGN some original **DOODLE PATTERNS** of your own!

Doodle something... BORING.

yawn!

GORGEOUS, DARLING!

LEARN TO ♥ DRAW

Follow the steps below to draw a BUSY BEE and a BEAUTIFUL BUTTERFLY.

step 1	step 2	step 3	You try it!

Shop till you drop!

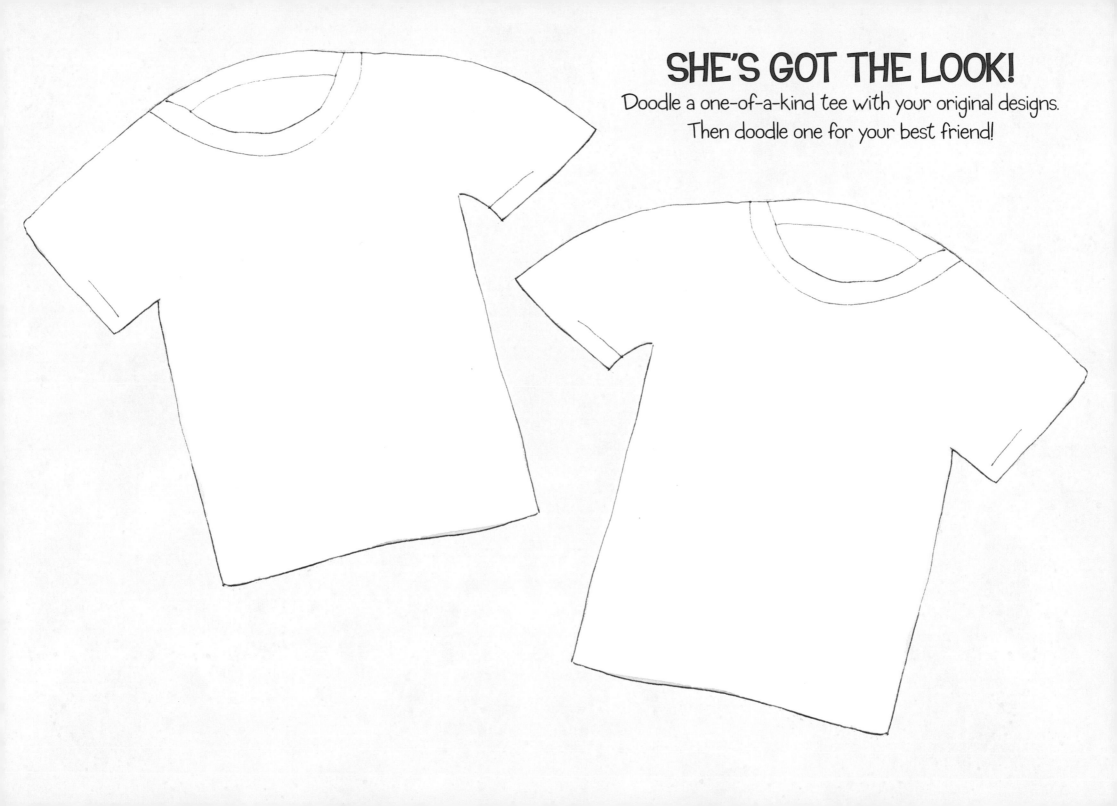

SHE'S GOT THE LOOK!
Doodle a one-of-a-kind tee with your original designs.
Then doodle one for your best friend!

TIME FOR SOME FUN IN THE SUN!

Fill in these **WORDS** with **DOODLES.**

PARTY HIP

AWESOME

LAUGH

GREAT

YUMMY

WILD

GROOVY

BOW WOW!

Complete each dog.

LEARN TO ♥ DRAW

Follow the steps below to draw a **BABY BLUEBIRD** and a **FLOWERY PLANT.**

step 1	step 2	step 3	You try it!

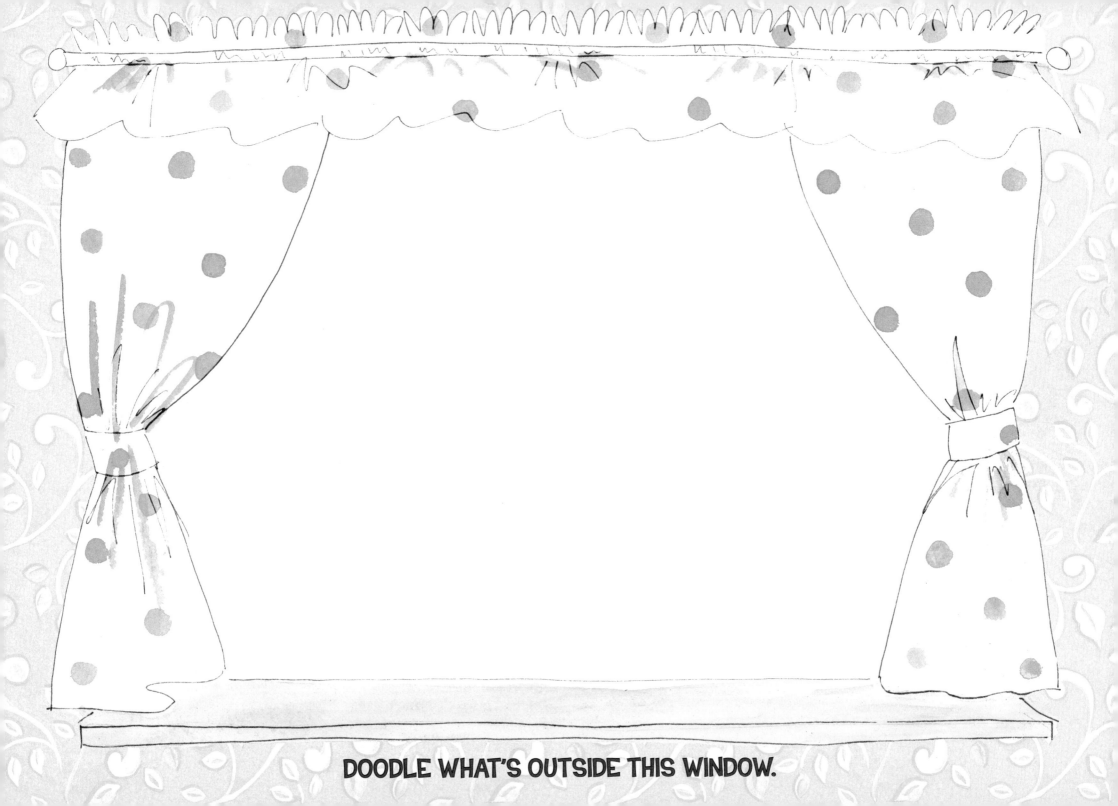

DOODLE WHAT'S OUTSIDE THIS WINDOW.

CAN YOU SAVE THE DAY? DOODLE A...

SUPERHERO, SIDEKICK, AND Villain.

CHECK OUT THIS topsy-turvy ALPHABET!

a b c d e f g h i j k l m n
o p q r s t u v w x y z . ! ? ,

TRACE the letters and words below.

a b c d e f g h i j k l m n
o p q r s t u v w x y z . ! ? ,

fierce   enthusiastic   awesome   hooray

Use what you've learned to **DOODLE WORDS OF YOUR OWN!**

PHOTO BOOTH

If you took
YOUR PETS
into a photo booth,
what would the
pictures look like?

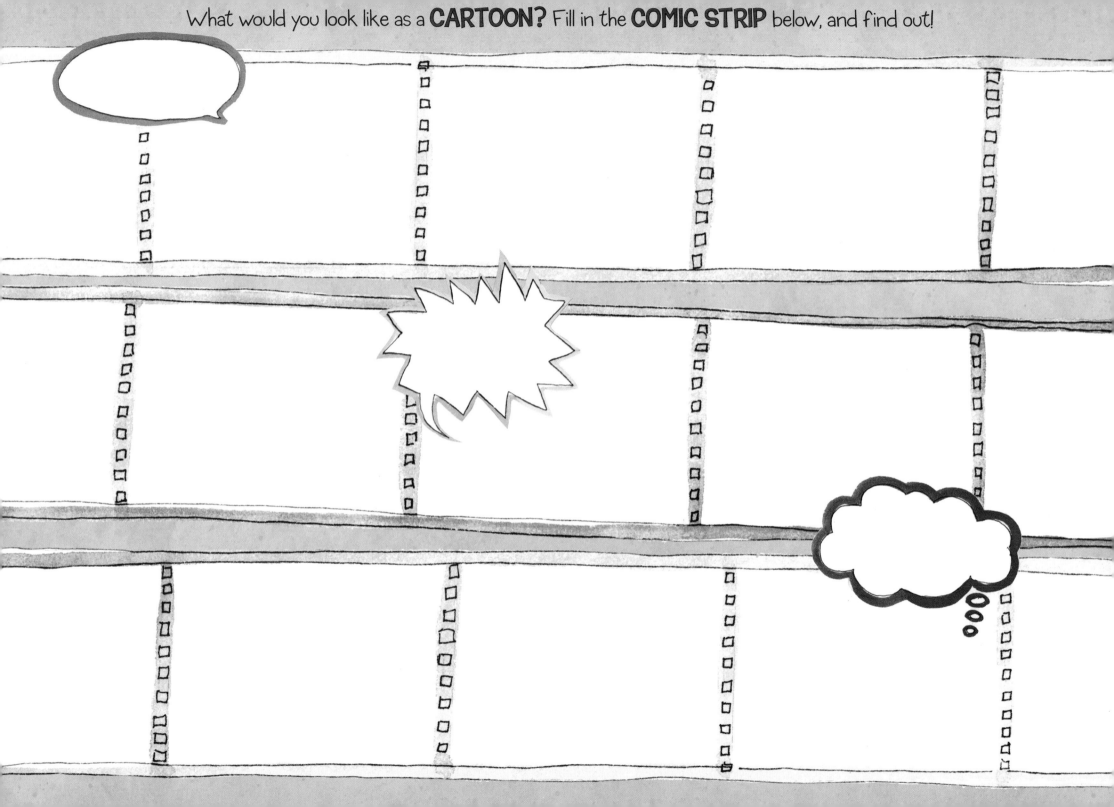

TIME FOR SOMETHING SWEET!

What's for dessert?

Space Doodles!

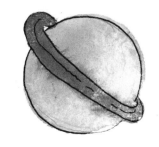

Fill in these **WORDS** with **DOODLES.**

FUN HAPPY COOL AMAZING SWEET SILLY LUCKY

Deep Sea Doodles!